MEL BAY'S COMPLETE
irish tin whistle book

by Mizzy McCaskill & Dona Gilliam

CD Contents

1. *The Chanter's Tune*   3:13
The Merry Harriers
The Threepenny Bit
Guitar: John C. Fishell
Slow Piece/Reels — Susato Whistle

2. *Brian the Brave (Poll Hapenny)* 2:34
Hornpipe — Schultz Whistle

3. *When I Followed a Lass*   3:28
Barrack Hill
Air/Jig — Air: Abell Whistle
Jig: Mel Bay Whistle

4. *The Dear Irish Boy*   5:24
Guitar: John C. Fishell
Voice: Mizzy McCaskill
Air — Susato Low A Whistle

5. *Tomgraney Castle*   4:31
The Honeysuckle
The Rights of Man
Hornpipes — Sweetone Whistle

6. *Sheebeg Sheemore*   3:10
The Stile of Ballylanders
Alexander's Hornpipe
Air/Reel/Hornpipe — Abell Whistle

7. *Up Stairs in a Tent*   2:15
After the Sun Goes Down
Sam's Girls
Reels — Soodlum's Mello D Whistle

8. *The Liverpool Hornpipe*   5:08
Harvest Home
Hornpipes — Shaw Whistles: Low D,
Low G,
Low A, D; Generation Whistle: G

9. *Get Up Old Woman and Shake
Yourself*   4:51
A Fig for a Kiss
Tobin's Favorite
Jigs — Copeland Whistle

10. *Agnus Dei*   4:57
Voice: Andy Warren
Thanksgiving
Larry Grogan
Chant/Slow Piece/Jig
Walton's Golden Tone — C Whistle

11. *The Hunt*   2:42
Set Dance — Pocket Companion Whistle

12. *Molly Put the Kettle On*   3:45
The Tunpike Gate
The Green Mountain
Reels — Feadog Whistle

13. *The New Potatoes*   3:09
Tie the Ribbons
The Belfast Lasses
Reels — Copeland Whistle

Photography by Dee Dee Niarhos, Mount Crowford, VA
Cover Designed by Wade Lough, Graphic Designer

This book is available either by itself or packaged with a companion audio and/or video recording. If you have purchased the book only, you may wish to purchase the recordings separately. The publisher strongly recommends using a recording along with the text to assure accuracy of interpretation and make learning easier and more enjoyable.

Visit us on the Web at www.melbay.com — E-mail us at email@melbay.com

there beside the weed and thistle,
a dog, a man and his tin whistle.

contents

about the whistle

The tin whistle or penny whistle is indigenous to the British Isles where it gained popularity as a folk instrument in the nineteenth century. Whistle playing was taught in the aural tradition, hence few methods or materials for the instrument were published until the mid-twentieth century when Irish folk music underwent a revival and the need to document aural traditions became important.

The tin whistle is part of a large family of whistle flutes or fipple flutes—those instruments which use a fipple or block in the windway to split the air stream and create a tone. Tin whistles are further categorized as six-holed, vertical, fipple flutes (i.e. fipple flutes with six holes that are held upright). Fipple flutes have been popular for centuries, and many early fipple flutes were called flageolets. In the seventeenth century the term flageolet was used to describe a French-made instrument with a fipple headpiece, four finger-holes on the front, and two thumb-holes on the back. At the turn of the nineteenth century an English-made flageolet appeared with a differing arrangement of tone-holes; some instruments had six finger-holes on the top of the tube and others had additional thumb-holes and key work. The label "flageolet" characterizes a wide variety of fipple flutes and it is still retained by some manufacturers of tin whistles who feel that the term more appropriately describes an instrument that does not fit the categories of tin or penny. Nineteenth century whistles were made of tin and sold for a nominal fee (perhaps a British penny), and the acquired names of tin whistle and penny whistle have endured to this day.

Examples of early six-holed vertical fipple flutes include those made of celluloid, wood, and metal alloys.

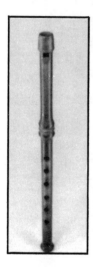

One-piece, cylindrical bore.
Wood (possibly pear).
Purchased in Switzerland, 1928.
Library of Congress.
Dayton C. Miller Collection
(#806).

Celluloid, with brown mouthpiece
(underside) and black rings.
Purchased in 1926.
Pitched in D.
One in a set of three pitched in
D, F, and G.
Front Marking: „Herculite" U-Paris
Back Marking: Re
Library of Congress.
Dayton C. Miller Collection (#608).

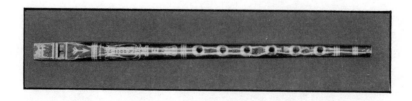

Early to mid-twentieth century tin whistle labeled *Calura*.
Made in Germany. Pitched in E. Private collection.

Traditional Irish tin whistles are made in two distinctive styles:

cylindrical

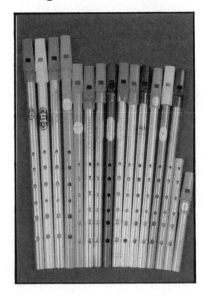

1) A **cylindrical** metal (brass, aluminum, nickel-plated brass) tube with a plastic fipple headpiece.

From left:
Walton's Brass-C, Walton's Golden Tin Whistle-C, Soodlum's-C, Perri-C, Perri-D, Soodlum's Mello-D, Soodlum's-D, Walton's Little Black Whistle-D, Feadog-D, Mel Bay-D, Oak-D, Clare-D, Pocket Companion-D, Galway-D, Eagle-D

---

conical

2) A **conical**, seamed, tin or enameled tin tube with:
   a) a wooden or plastic block inserted to form the windway, or
   b) a plastic fipple headpiece.

     From left:
          Clarke-C
          Clarke-C
          Sweetone-C
          Sweetone- D
          Sweet-D

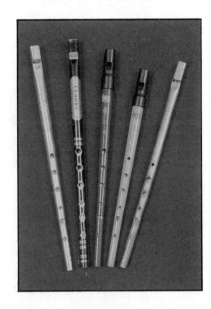

Variations on these two themes occur regularly: the bore size changes (larger bored instruments have a mellower, richer sound); the tube changes from brass, to aluminum, to nickel-silver, to copper, and other alloys; the tube is molded from plastic; the entire instrument is made of hard-woods; and the instrument is made in two sections for ease in tuning.

More expensive handmade instruments are also available. They are fashioned from hardwoods or metal and are hand-tuned (voiced). Wooden models can have metal ferrules and mouthpiece caps as well as metal slides that insert into the headpiece for ease of tuning. Interchangeable joints of varying lengths are often made for playing in different keys. The handmade instruments are also known for their louder, full-bodied sounds and ease of tuning. They exhibit all of the same fine craftsmanship used by makers of wooden recorders and flutes.

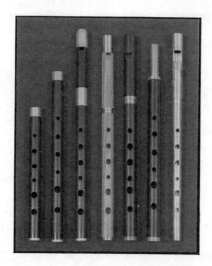

From left:

Abell, with interchangeable joints for E Flat, C, and D

Schultz-D

O'Riordan, with interchangeable joints for C and D

Copeland-D, jointed for tuning

Six-holed fipple flutes continue to fascinate hobbyists and instrument makers, and whistles of all shapes, sizes, and materials are available from both commercial and private makers.

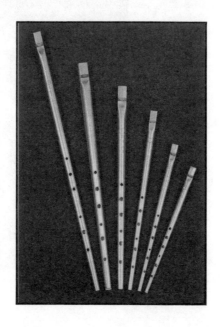

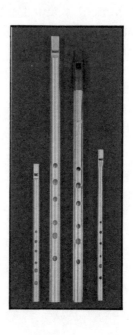

Susato Whistles

From Left:
Low D, Low G,
Low A, B Flat, C, D

Shaw Whistles

From Left:
Low D, Low F,
Low G, Low A, C, D

From Left:
Overton D,
Overton Low D,
Howard Low D,
Hohner-D

keys

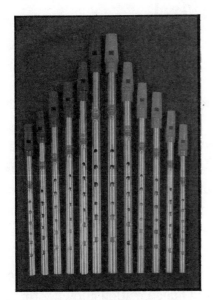

Six-holed instruments such as the whistle are fully chromatic, i.e. a complete chromatic scale can be played within the given range of the instrument. This is only accomplished, however, through complicated half-holing and cross-fingerings. The fingering configuration is easier to manuever in certain keys, and it is for this reason that whistles are pitched in different keys. The standard keys have become: B Flat, C, D, E Flat, F, and G.

Fingering charts found in this tutor are written for whistles pitched in D (when all of the tone holes are covered the concert pitch D sounds).

Generation Whistles: Brass Set and Nickel-Plated Brass Set
Sets Pitched in Keys (as shown above): G, F, E Flat, D, C, B Flat/B Flat, C, D, E Flat, F, and G

One can play with a variety of folk or traditional instruments by playing whistles pitched in different keys. Each whistle plays "comfortably" (without too much cross-fingering or half-holing) in three keys: the tonic key, and closely-related keys a perfect fourth and perfect fifth higher. For example: D whistles play easily in the keys of D Major, G Major, and A Major.

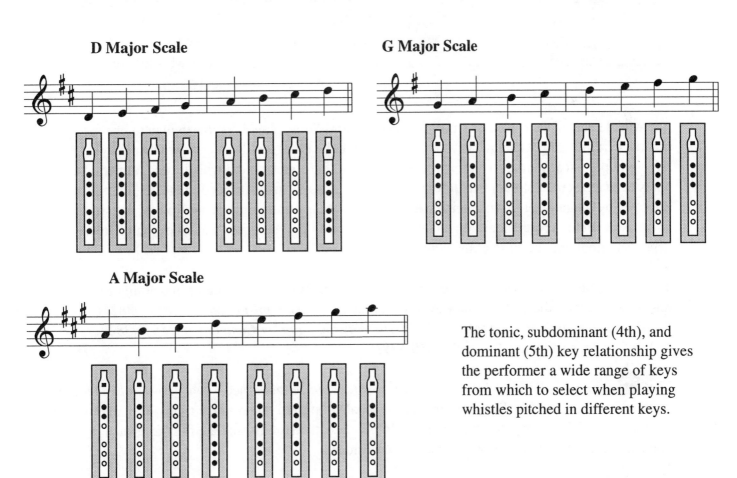

D Major Scale

G Major Scale

A Major Scale

The tonic, subdominant (4th), and dominant (5th) key relationship gives the performer a wide range of keys from which to select when playing whistles pitched in different keys.

⊠ fundamentals ⊠

The whistle is traditionally fingered by placing the first three fingers of the left hand on the top three tone-holes, and the first three fingers of the right hand on the bottom three tone-holes. The placement of the hands can be reversed, but it makes the transition to other wind instruments such as the transverse flute, saxophone, or clarinet more difficult.

The pads of the fingers are used to cover the tone-holes, with a curved hand position allowing for ease of fingering. Some traditional players flatten the fingers and employ more motion from the knuckle when playing. The aim is to find a hand position that will allow both comfort and dexterity of the fingers.

The instrument rests on the thumbs. Players who do not find this position secure enough for comfort and ease of playing may fashion a thumb-rest from a piece of cork taped to the whistle. Some commercially available whistles are made with thumbpiece attachments.

The whistle headpiece is placed gently between the lips. Some players prefer to play to one side—a holdover from piping technique or a means of hearing the tones loudly in one ear when playing in a large group. A steady stream of air is needed to control the sound on the whistle, and higher octave notes need a faster air stream than lower octave notes. Crisp, clean attacks on note beginnings may be achieved by tonguing as if whispering the word "too." Many traditional players prefer to start a note or phrase with the breath alone. When this practice is used the sharpness and precision of attack is dependant upon the response of the whistle itself.

This text requires familiarity with conventional music notation. For assistance in learning to read music consult these other Mel Bay Publications: *Tinwhistle for Beginners (MB #93821), Children's Tinwhistle Method (MB #95305), The Whistler's Pocket Companion (MB #93820),* or *You Can Teach Yourself Tinwhistle (MB #95361).*

The 🎼 symbol will be used throughout this text to indicate those pieces which have been recorded on the accompanying CD. Recorded pieces are usually repeated two or three times. The articulation markings given for each piece approximate closely the articulations used the first time each tune is played. Variations may occur on subsequent repetitions.

Irish music

The bulk of traditional Irish folk music consists of dance tunes and airs that date from the seventeenth to nineteenth centuries. Many of the dance tunes (jigs, reels, and hornpipes) adhere to a sixteen measure, binary (two-part) form. The first eight measures (A section) are known as the *tune*, and the second eight measures (B section) are known as the *turn*. Note the formal markings in the following jig:

The newmarried couple

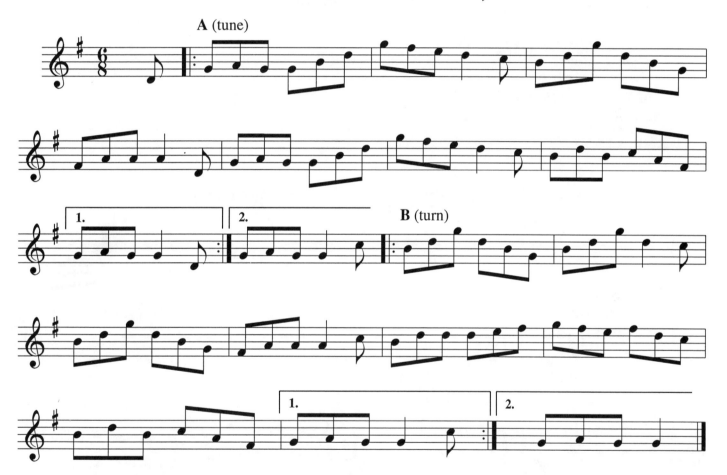

As in the above example, each section of the music is usually repeated (doubled). If a section has similar phrases (exact repetitions), it may be played only one time through (singled). Entire pieces are repeated many times in the dance setting until the dance concludes. In solo performances of jigs, reels, and hornpipes, each piece is repeated two or three times and is usually linked to other dances of the same type.

Beyond large formal structures, specific dance types have distinguishing characteristics.

jigs

There are three varieties of the jig: the **double jig** in ⅜ time, the **single jig** in ⅜ or ⅛ time, and the **hop jig** (also called a **slip jig**) in ⅜ time.

double jig

The **double jig** is delineated from other jigs by its characteristic rhythm of repeated eighth notes:

(At the player's discretion, repeated eighth notes may also be interpreted with a rhythm.)

The A and B sections of the double jig will use the running eighth note figure predominantly throughout, with the last bar changing to:

The last measure frequently repeats the tonic note, and the most common ending will repeat the tonic on the last two or three notes of the piece. This is seen in the following double jig:

the first night in america

single jig

The **single jig** incorporates more ♩ ♪ ♩ ♪ rhythms in its A and B sections than the double jig. The last bar of each section often ends on a final ♩. ♩ rhythm. This can be seen in the following single jig:

come in from the rain

slip jig

The **slip** or **hop jig** uses various groupings of 𝅘𝅥 𝅘𝅥𝅮𝅘𝅥𝅮 𝅘𝅥 , 𝅘𝅥 𝅘𝅥𝅮 , and 𝅘𝅥. rhythms.

It is distinguished by its $\frac{9}{8}$ time signature.

A large number of Irish dance tunes end on a note designed to lead into another strain or to a repeated section. The performer wishing to end a piece written in this manner will appropriately select the tonic as the final note of resolution. Note how the following slip jig requires some reworking to this effect. Different endings can be added by the performer. An extra measure can be tagged on at the end, or the final few notes of the piece may be rewritten until they comfortably resolve to the tonic. A suggested ending that resolves to tonic is given for the following slip jig:

dress her out in fine clothes

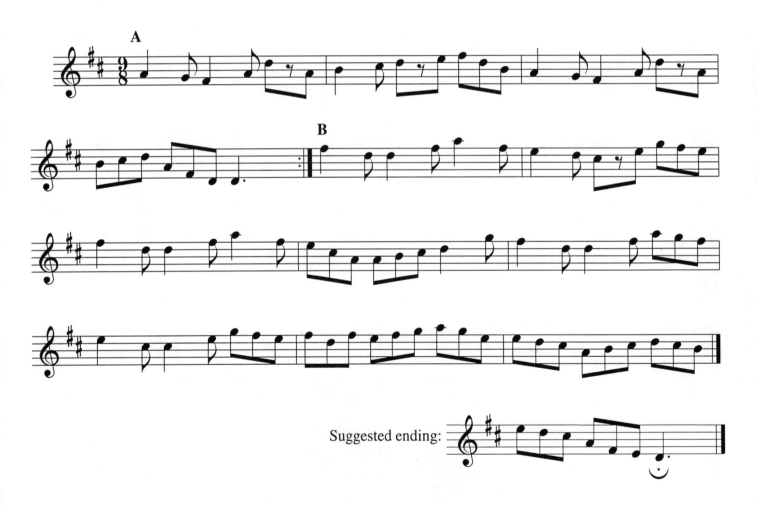

Suggested ending:

reel

The **reel** is the most popular genre of tunes played by traditional instrumentalists.
It is often played at a fast tempo, consequently it appeals to the virtuoso player.
Strings of repeated eighth notes
are associated with the reel.

Performance practice allows the substitution of dotted

or triplet figures, although the reel is traditionally notated with
even eighth notes as in the following example:

the salamanca reel

hornpipe

The **hornpipe** is played at a slower tempo than the reel, and in a more heavily accented fashion.

It is customary for the closing bars of each section in a hornpipe to end with a ♩ ♩ ♩ rhythm.

The dotted eighth/sixteenth rhythm 𝅘𝅥𝅭♪ 𝅘𝅥𝅭♪ 𝅘𝅥𝅭♪ 𝅘𝅥𝅭♪ usually prevails in the performance

of the hornpipe, although it is frequently notated as a pattern of straight eighth notes.

The hornpipe may also be distinguished by its formal structure. While it is often in two-part (AB) form, extended forms (ABC, ABCD, AABA, etc.) may differentiate it from the reel. An example of a hornpipe that is intended to end on the A section follows:

the belfast hornpipe

The *D.C.* marking in the last measure indicates that the player should return to the beginning and play until the fermata sign (⌣).

14

set dance

Set dances were usually written for a particular dance. They are distinguished from other dance forms because the sections vary in length and/or time signature. The following set dance, for example, has an extended twelve measure B section:

madam bonaparte

garden of daisies

(Set dance with sixteen measure B section)

16

Performance
Practice

Mere familiarity with the structural outline of an Irish tune does not allow the untrained player to render a tune satisfactorily. It is by understanding how stylistic elements are applied to Irish music that one can approximate a more traditional approach to playing. Listening to live and/or recorded performances, studying with traditional players, and working through written methods for learning to play in the Irish style is the only way to gain an accurate understanding of performance practice.

Stylistic elements affecting traditional performances include: tempo, rhythm, phrasing, ornamentation, and the process of variation. Absent from the list is dynamic contrast (varying levels of loudness). This is difficult to achieve on the whistle, and is usually not a consideration when playing in the ensemble (group) setting.

tempo

The tempo (speed of performance) of a piece can vary due to the mood and skill of the performer. When learning to play a tune, it is best to practice at a slower tempo if note accuracy is of concern. It must be remembered that selection of a tempo is flexible, and that it can alter the character of a tune completely. A reel when played extremely fast can be a solo artist's tour de force, yet it might be unsuitable for those trying to dance a reel to the music. The player must decide for himself which tempo best fits the character and use of the piece. Listening to recorded versions of the same piece by different artists will give one a better idea of how tempo can vary within acceptable limits.

Rhythm

Written sources of traditional Irish music present the music in its purest form, without ornamentation or rhythmic alteration. As the previous discussion of Irish music indicated it is common to vary notated rhythms. In common ($\frac{4}{4}$) or cut time (₵), running eighth notes

may be interpreted as (...) or (...)

In compound times ($\frac{6}{8}$, $\frac{9}{8}$, $\frac{12}{8}$) a pattern of three eighth notes (...) may be interpreted as (...) The player should note that rhythmic variation is not employed by all players, nor is it used all of the time by any one player. It is up to the performer to decide which type of variation (if any) will enhance the rhythmic flow of the tune.

phrasing

A phrase marking in music is similar to a sentence in prose. It indicates a complete musical thought and is used to give structure and continuity to the performance of a piece.

phrase marking

Written sources of traditional music do not include phrase markings because they can vary widely, and their placement contributes to the unique stylistic interpretation of a tune. As a general rule, the symmetrical construction of most dance tunes (two eight bar sections) allows a regular break in phrasing to occur every two or four measures as in the following example:

anotheR jig will do!

Phrasing is not always confined by the bar line, and the skillful musician will use the phrase to place emphasis on certain notes or to add rhythmic interest to a tune. Notes at the end of one phrase, for example, may be used as pick-up notes to the next phrase. This type of "phrasing across the bar line" is a common characteristic of traditional performance practice. It is shown in *The Smoky House*.

the smoke house

Common indicators for appropriate phrase markings may also be observed
in the above example. Notes of longer duration towards the end of a measure
often serve as phrase endings and/or places to take a breath. Each quarter note
in the example above serves as a phrase ending. The contour (shape) of the
musical line may also indicate a logical point at which to end or begin a phrase.
In the above example a large leap after a line of descending notes indicates the
ending point of one phrase and the beginning of a new phrase. In any case the
phrasing should assist the performer in playing with expression and cause little
interruption in the flow of the musical line. More often than not the traditional
player has an approach to phrasing where the rule is "Keep the music flowing
and take a breath when you need it—the rest will take care of itself."

ornamentation

slides, cuts, short rolls,
long rolls, double graces,
triple graces, triplets

slide

The **slide** is used to give emphasis to a note or phrase, and it is performed by gradually sliding the finger off of a tone hole. The slide can only occur between two adjacent notes, and it is performed by the finger positioned over the lowest covered tone hole. For example:

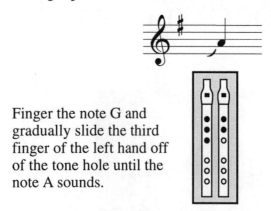

Finger the note G and gradually slide the third finger of the left hand off of the tone hole until the note A sounds.

The finger can slide in any direction, and the player must decide which direction he/she prefers for comfort and ease of playing. There is not a standard notational symbol for the slide, however, the symbol shown above will be used to indicate a slide in the remaining portion of this text.

o'connell's lamentation

cut

The **cut** is a grace note, or a note played quickly **before** the principal note. It is used to:

a) emphasize or accentuate a particular note, or

b) to separate two notes of the same pitch.

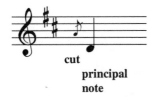

cut

principal
note

The term **cut** refers to a note **above** the principal note.* Cuts are commonly performed on the notes **D, E, F#, G, A,** and **B**. Numerous fingerings will produce cuts, and it is advisable to experiment in order to find the fingerings that will achieve the desired effect as well as facilitate ease in playing your instrument. A standard fingering chart for cuts follows along with tunes for practicing the cut. The fingerings given in the tunes for practice will allow you to maneuver cuts without slowing down to learn all of the fingering options.

*A grace note **below** the principal note is called a **tip** or **strike**. The tip is used most frequently in the context of a long or short roll (see section discussing these ornaments). The tip may also be used to separate two notes of the same pitch. In these instances the tip is fingered with standard fingerings.

tip

principal
note

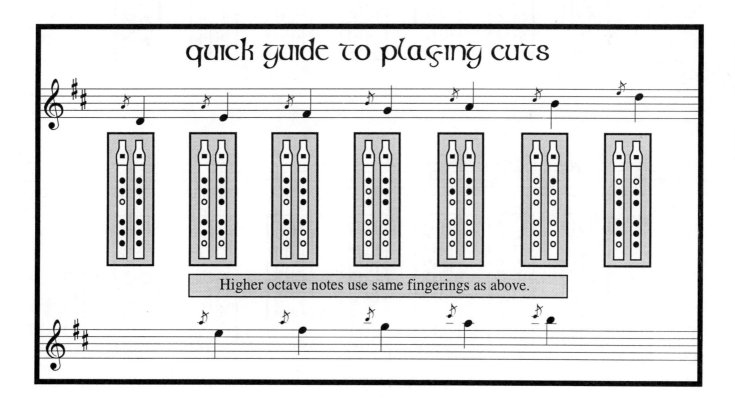

quick guide to playing cuts

Higher octave notes use same fingerings as above.

CUTS

The pitch of the cut shows the pitch that sounds when the note is cut.

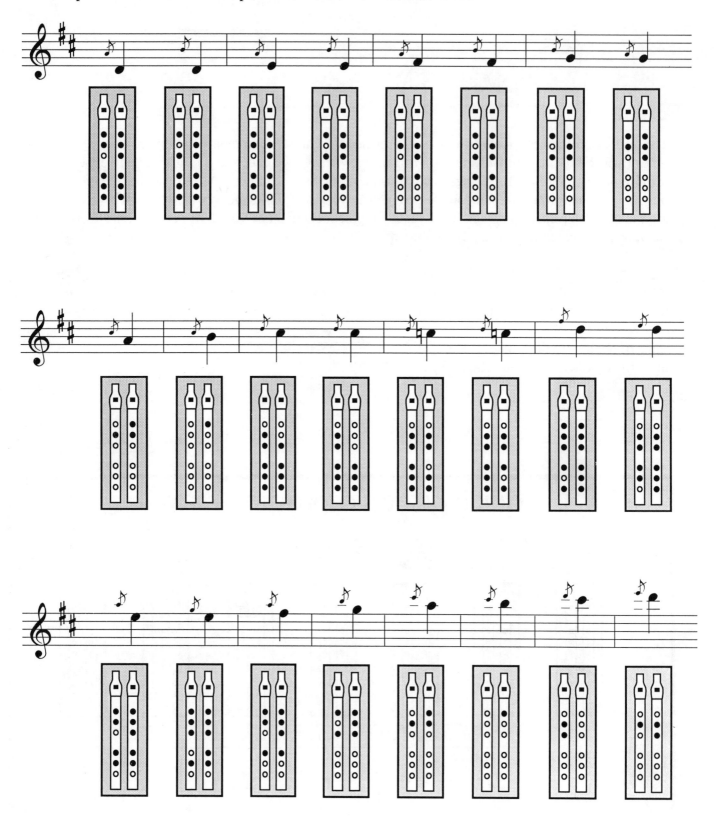

24

cuts between two notes of the same pitch

When the cut is used to separate two notes of the same pitch it is not necessary to rearticulate (tongue) the cut. It is played under one breath.

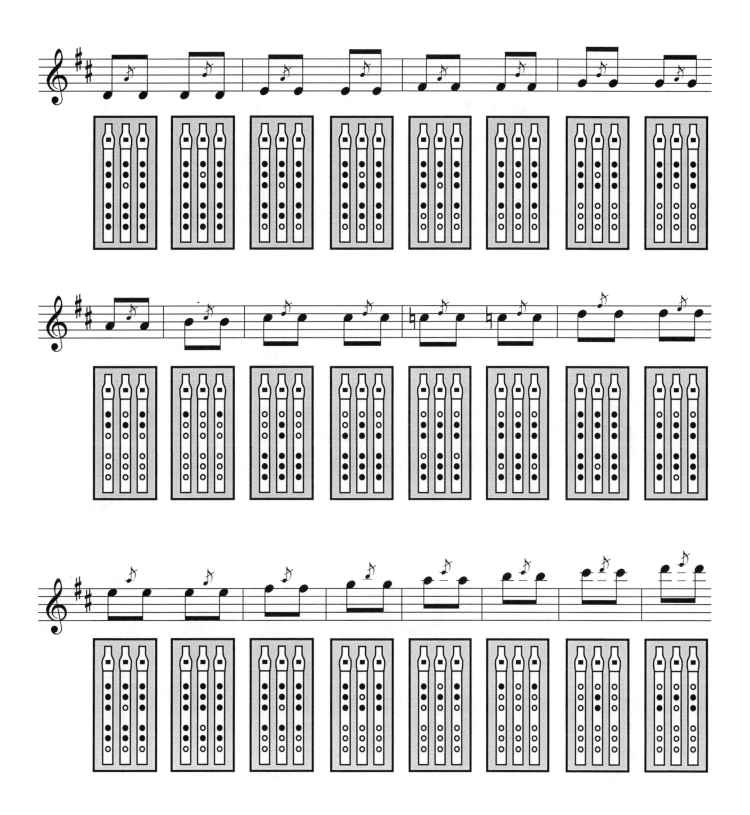

get up old woman and shake gourself

Tobin's Favorite

a fig for a kiss

* Exception to cut indicating its sounding pitch: The note B is cut with C# regardless of the key signature.

28

wheels of the world

double grace note fingerings

Double grace notes (also known as casadh) are similar to cuts between two notes of the same pitch except that the initial principal note is part of the ornament. Double grace note are played quickly **before** the principal note.

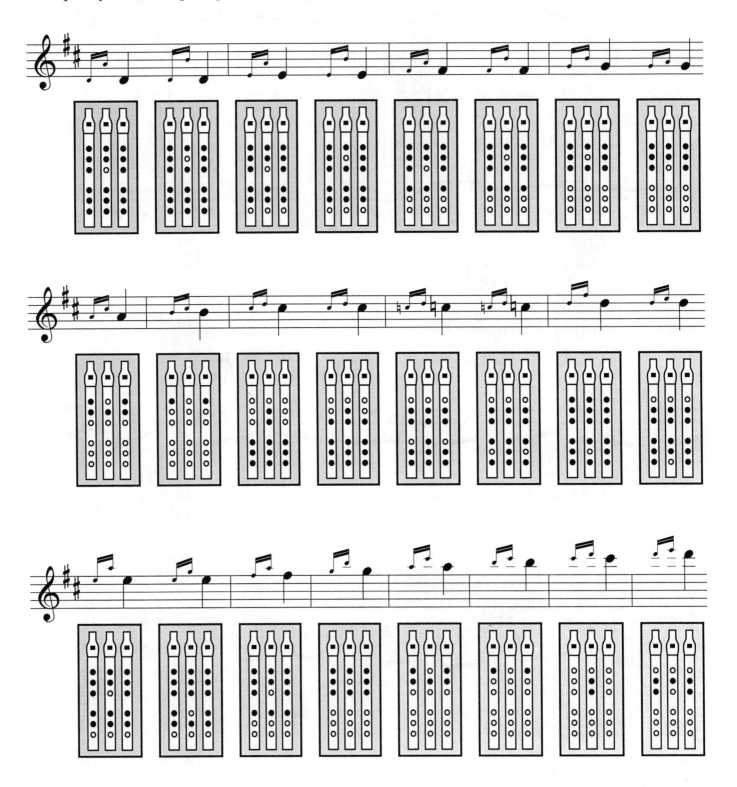

Another type of double grace note is familiar to classically trained musicians. It is formed by the principal note and its upper neighbor tone (scale tone directly above the principal note). It may be substituted for the double grace figure shown on the previous chart.

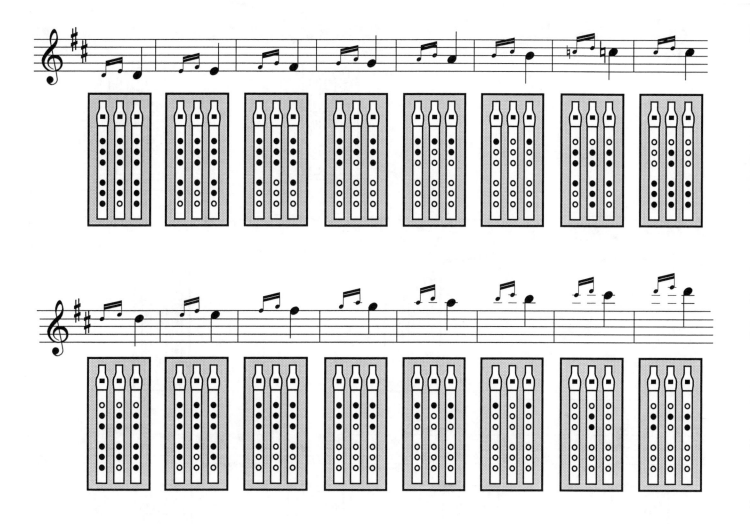

A less common double grace figure is formed by tipping the principal note (playing the scale tone directly below the principal note). Standard fingerings are used to perform these double grace figures.

Example: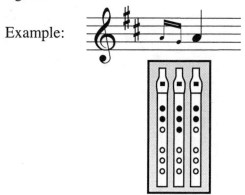

31

the humors of whiskey

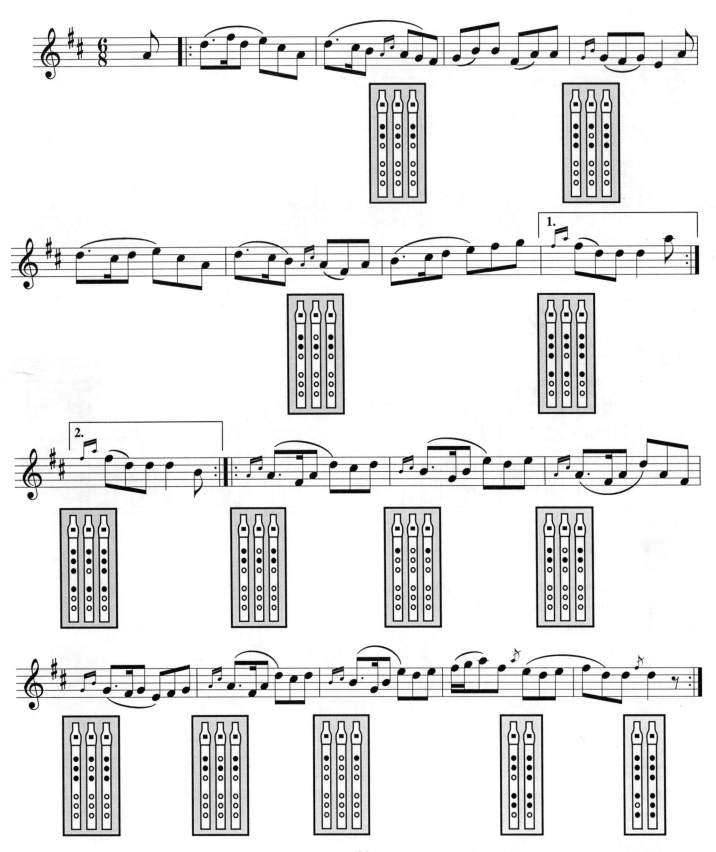

32

sweet biddy daly

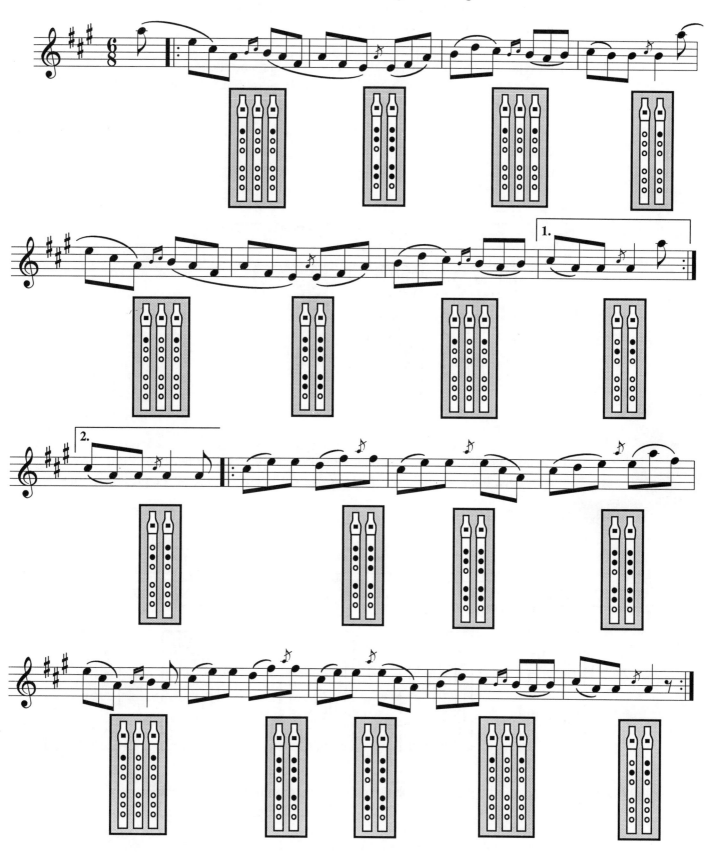

triple grace notes

The **triple grace note** ornament is used infrequently, however, it may be added where a variety of ornamentation is desired. Triple grace notes consist of three short notes played quickly **before** the principal note. There are two types of triple grace notes:

1) The first type is familiar to classically trained players, and it consists of an upper neighbor tone, the principal note, and an upper neighbor tone. Standard fingerings are used in the performance of this ornament.

Example:

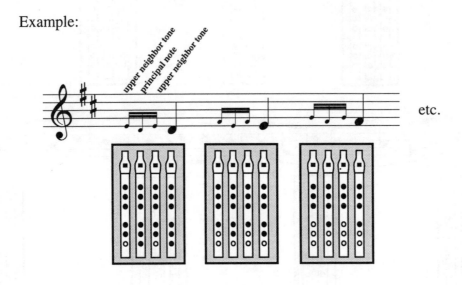

etc.

2) The second type stems from ornamentation used by pipers. It consists of a cut above the principal note, the principal note, and another **different** cut above the principal note.

Example:

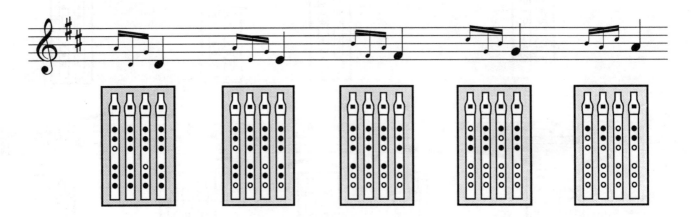

Note: The upper cuts can also be placed in ascending order as seen in the example above on the note A.

34

the hag by the fire

TRIPLETS

A **triplet** is a group of three notes played in the time of two notes of the same value.
It is usually indicated by the number three placed above or below the group of three notes.

Example:

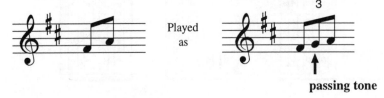

Triplets are used to:
1) Link notes separated by the interval of a third by filling in a passing tone.

2) To add motion to a longer note by:
   a. Playing the principal note, its upper neighbor tone,
      and the principal note.

   b. Playing a group of three staccato (tongued/detached) notes on the same pitch.

3) To transcend smoothly an ascending or descending musical line.
   Notes are filled in or repeated as in the following examples:

36

staccato triplets

When the performance tempo is fast, the player may have difficulty quickly tonguing each note of a staccato triplet. A multiple articulation pattern may be used in faster passages to substitute for single strokes of the tongue. This involves the use of unvoiced syllables. Select a group of syllables that best approximates a clearly articulated triplet.

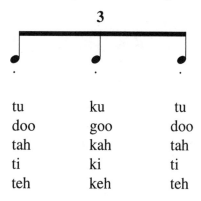

tu	ku	tu
doo	goo	doo
tah	kah	tah
ti	ki	ti
teh	keh	teh

Although this may be cumbersome at first, careful practice that emphasizes evenness of all syllables will allow fast passages to be played with ease.

harvest home

37

The placement of triplets in a piece can vary, and when triplets are added at different times in repeated sections of music they will contribute to the distinctive character of each version. Two versions of *The Liverpool Hornpipe* follow. Grey boxes indicate the presence of a triplet in the ornamented version.

the liverpool hornpipe

After playing through this example, experiment on your own with the placement of triplets.

the liverpool hornpipe

mollie mccarthy

the quarrelsome piper

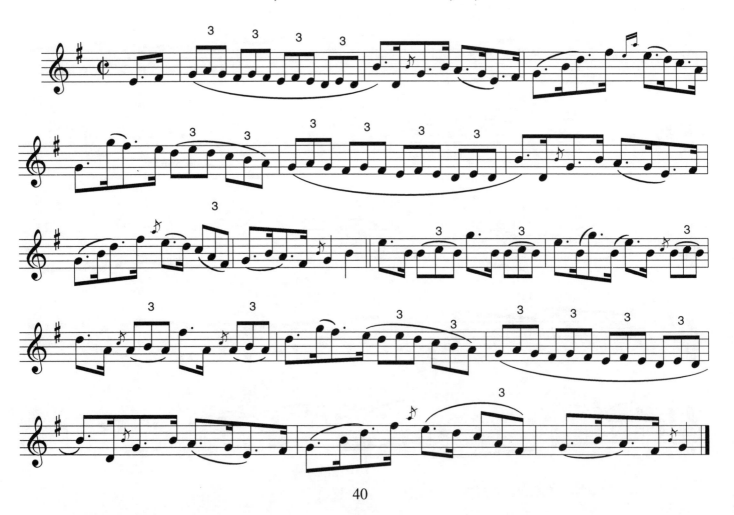

Pieces for the study and practice of cuts double graces and triplets

the hunt

τomgranes castle

the honeysuckle

the rights of man

44

the new potatoes

the belfast lasses

TIE THE RIBBONS

THE GREEN MOUNTAIN

46

ROLLS

The **roll** is an ornament that involves cutting and tipping a principal note. In each roll the principal note is ornamented with two grace notes: the first grace is above the principal note, and the second grace is below the principal note. The higher grace note is called a **cut**, and the lower grace note is called a **tip** or **strike**. The tip is usually the note directly below the principal note, and it retains the accidentals found in the key signature.

Long Roll

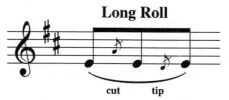

cut   tip

Short Roll

cut   tip

Short Roll

The short roll is used to ornament a quarter note or two eighth notes of the same pitch. It is performed and notated in a variety of ways:

1) As grace notes separating two eighth notes of the same pitch,

2) As triple grace notes,

3) As a triplet preceded by a grace note (sometimes called a graced triplet),

4) As four sixteenth notes,

Preferred Notation:

A ⌣ symbol (not to be confused with a bowing mark or fermata sign).

5) As a grace note preceding a dotted figure,

47

short roll fingerings

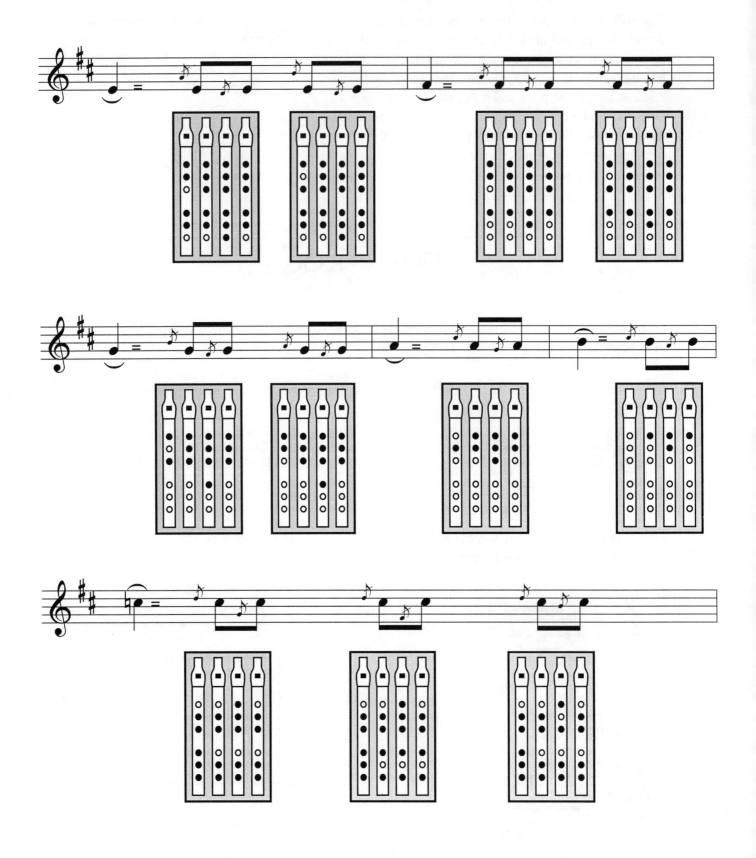

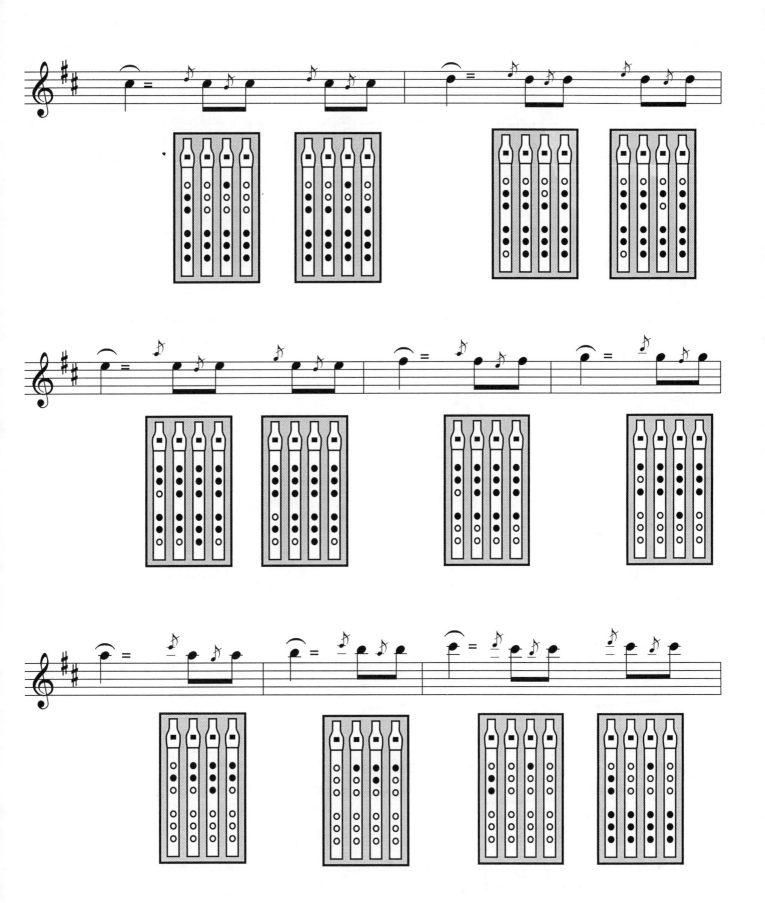

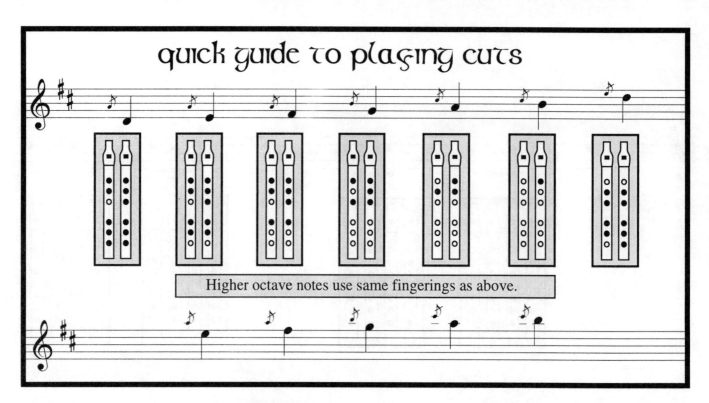

quick guide to playing cuts

Higher octave notes use same fingerings as above.

E short roll:

man of the house

F# short roll:

  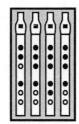

(High octave uses same fingering)

sam's girls

M.M./D.G.

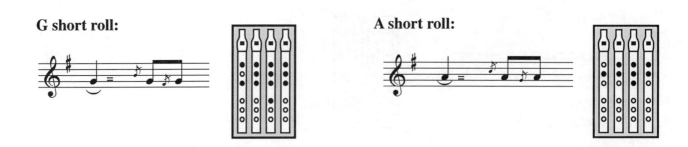

woman of the house

G short roll:

after the sun goes down

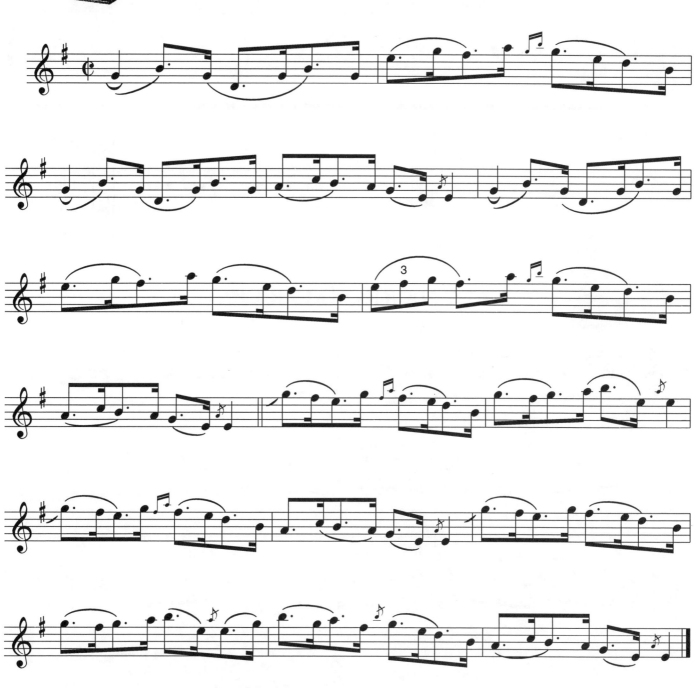

53

quick guide to playing cuts

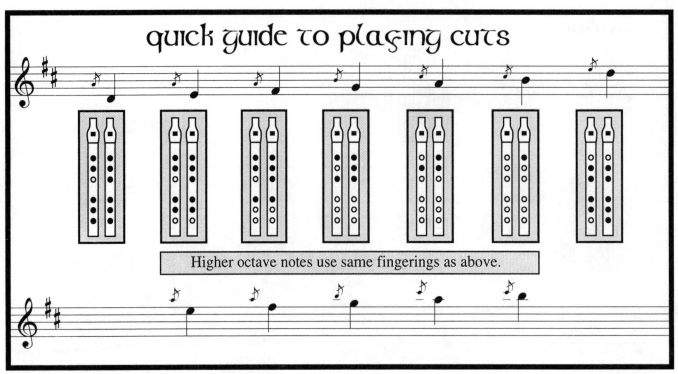

Higher octave notes use same fingerings as above.

G short roll:

A short roll:

the merry harriers

Suggested ending:

E short roll:

the stile of ballglanders

55

quick guide to playing cuts

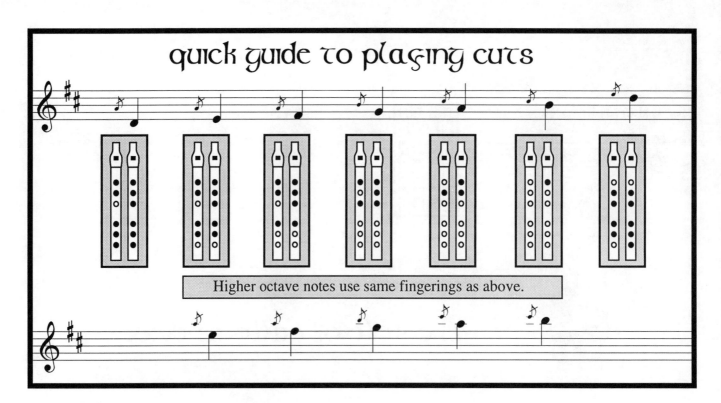

Higher octave notes use same fingerings as above.

B short roll:

the hornless cow

Short Rolls:

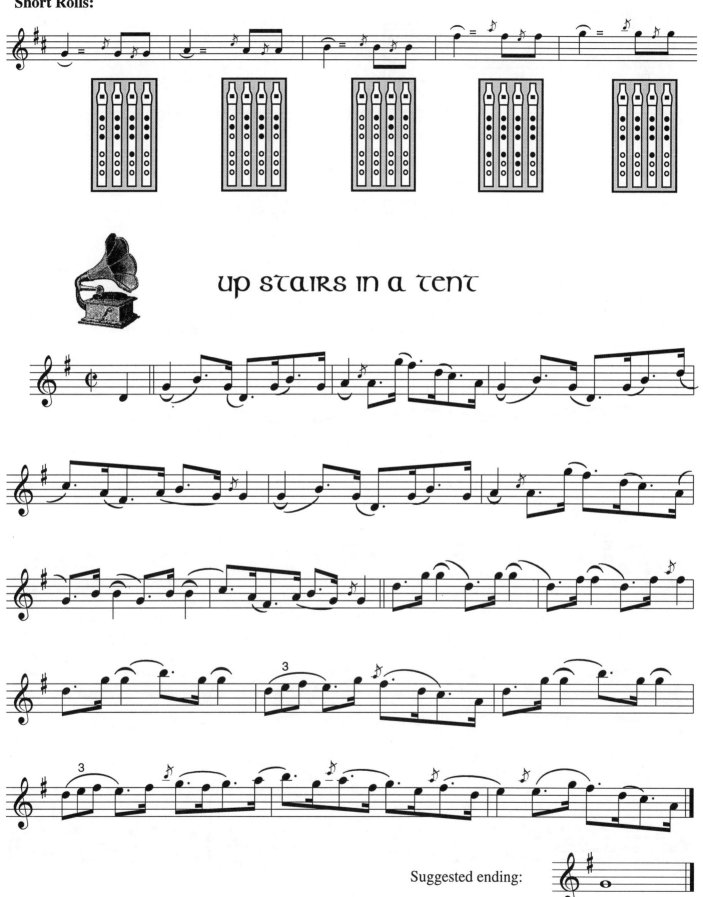

UP STAIRS IN A TENT

Suggested ending:

High G short roll:

captain oneill's

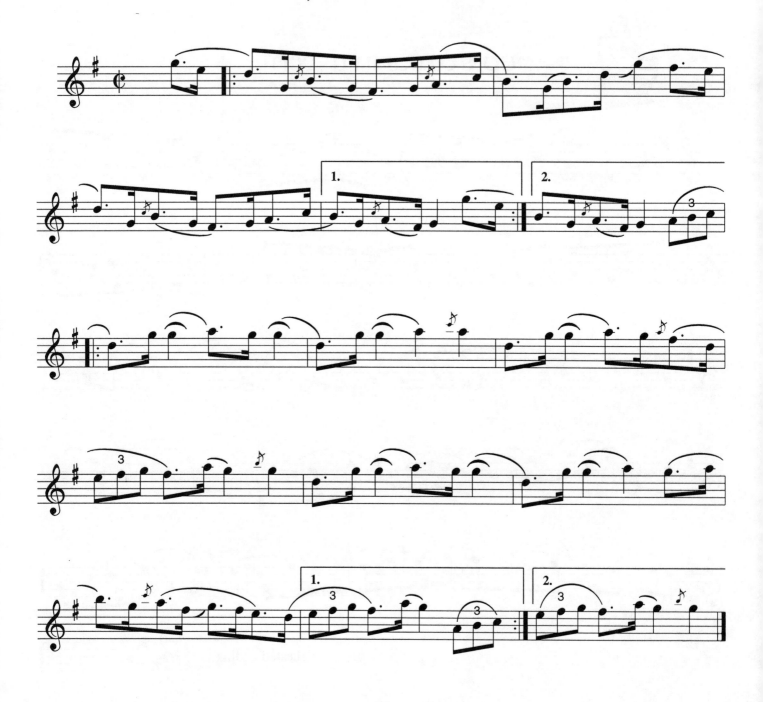

A short roll:

the cork hornpipe

A short roll:

(Higher octave uses same fingering)

dan mccarthg's fancg

Long Roll

The long roll is used to ornament the dotted quarter note in both compound ($\frac{6}{8}$, $\frac{9}{8}$ etc.) and simple (¢ , $\frac{4}{4}$ etc.) time. Like the short roll, the long roll is performed and notated in a variety of ways:

1) As grace notes separating three notes of the same pitch.

 or

2) As a triplet placed between two notes of the same pitch.

3) As thirty-second notes following a long principal note.

4) As a grupetto. The classically trained player will recognize the similarity of the long roll to the Baroque gruppetto. The gruppetto may be substituted for the long roll; however, it is not a preferred fingering since it uses an upper neighbor tone (note directly above the principal note) instead of a cut. The gruppetto figure uses standard fingerings throughout the range of the instrument.

5) As a quintuplet.

Preferred Notation:

A roll symbol.

The ⌣ or ⌢ symbol will be used to indicate a roll throughout the remaining portion of this text. A symbolic representation of the ornament encourages the player to rhythmically alter the roll to suit his/her taste. Listen to the performance of the rolls on the accompanying recording, and follow along in the music. You will soon acquire the ability to use the roll as a key element of ornamentation in the Irish style.

long roll fingerings

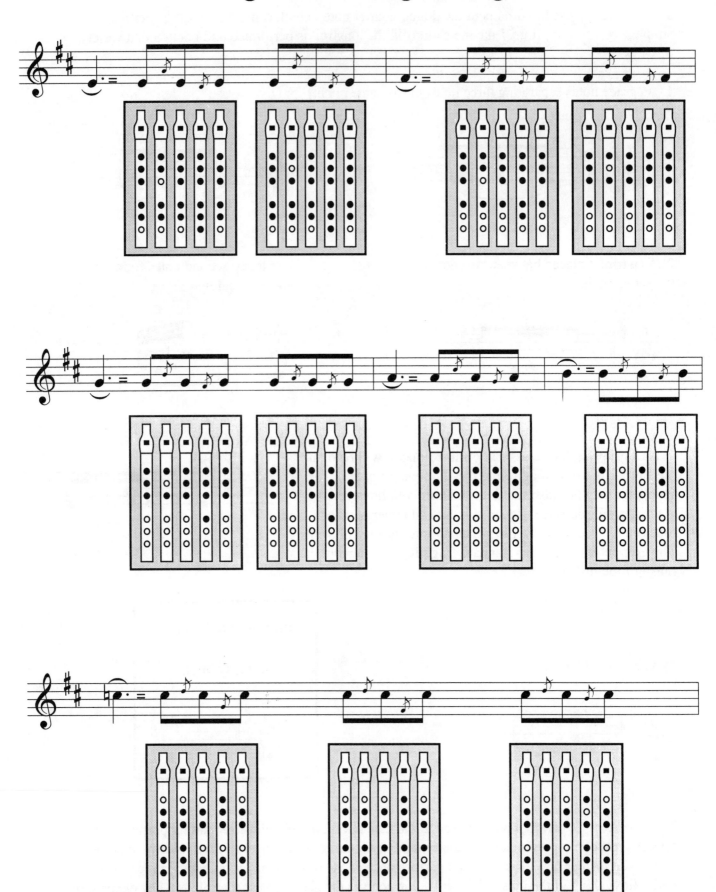

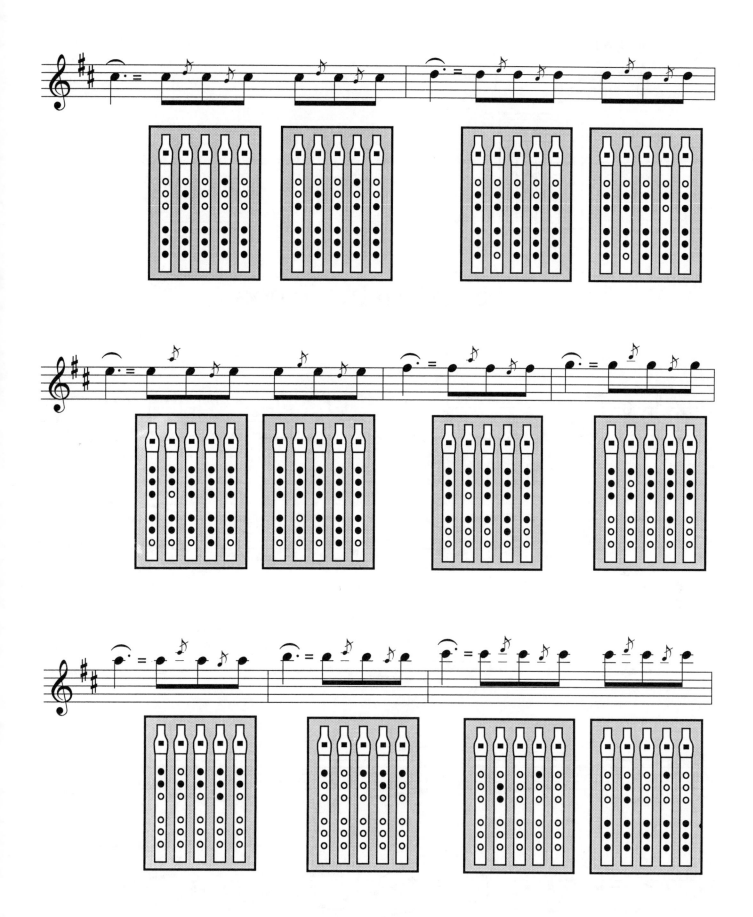

Note: Try other fingering combinations not listed above. Response to fingerings will vary on different instruments due to variations in bore size and tone-hole placement.

B long roll:

the yellow little bog

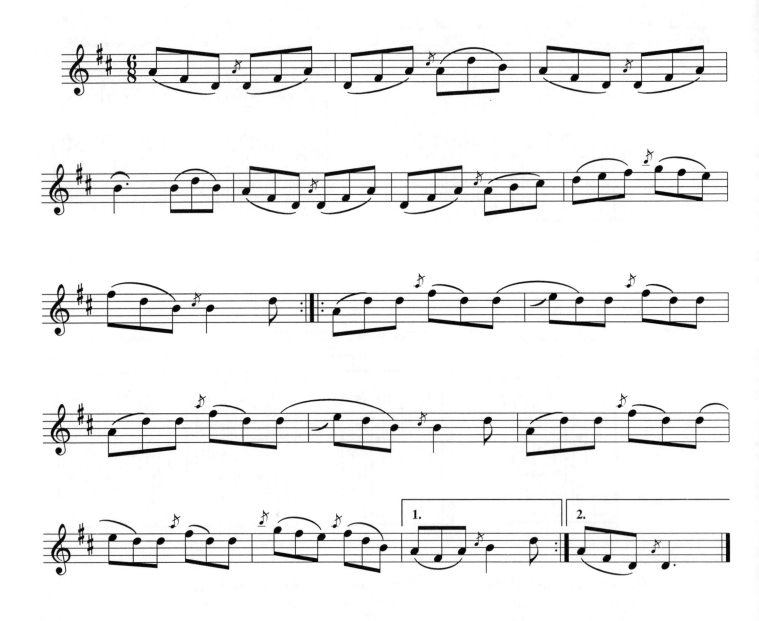

A long roll:

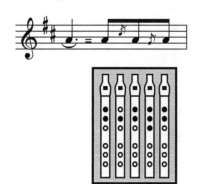

the turnpike gate

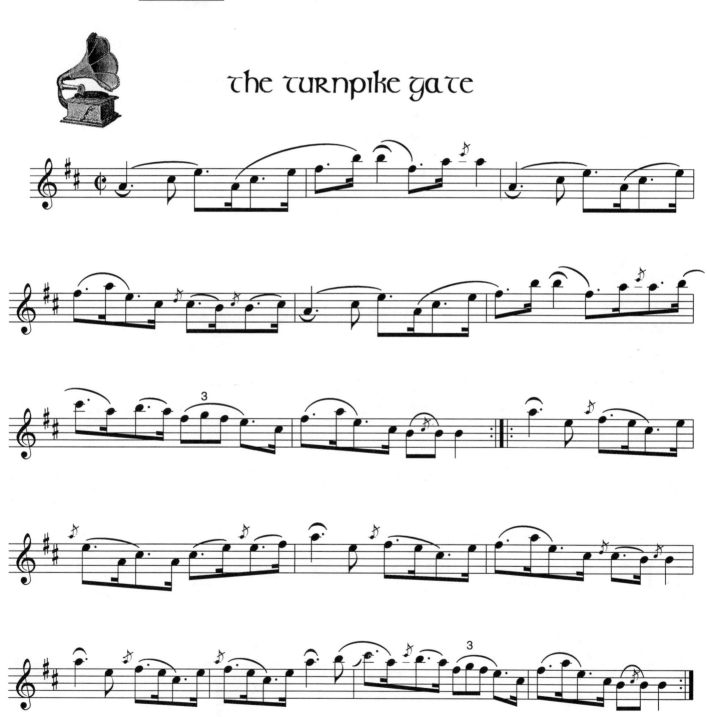

Long rolls:

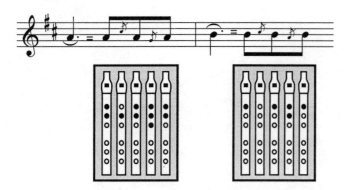

Reminder: When played at a fast tempo, the staccato eighth notes in the following piece may be played in the same manner as a staccato triplet. The use of certain unvoiced syllables can assist the player in clearly articulating each staccato note. Recommended syllables include:

tu	ku	tu
doo	goo	doo
tah	kah	tah
ti	ki	ti
teh	keh	teh

barrack hill

Long rolls:

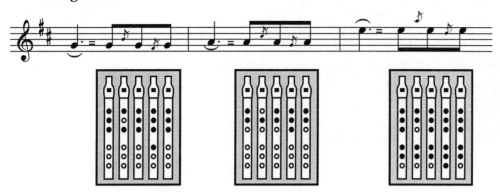

behind the bush in the garden

67

Long rolls:

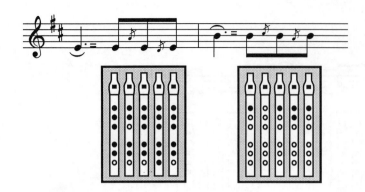

molly put the kettle on

Long rolls:

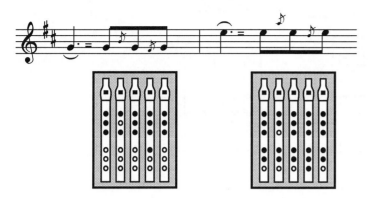

the teetotaller's reel

Long rolls:

 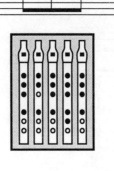 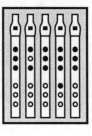

larrʒ ʒroʒan

70

Long rolls:

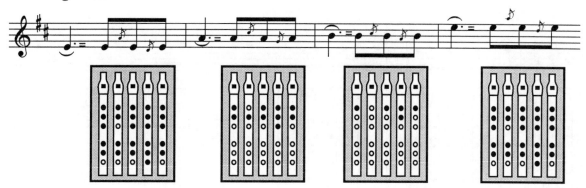

swinging round the circle

Long rolls:

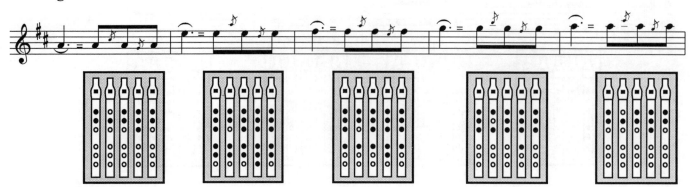

brian the brave (poll hapenng)

72

Long rolls:

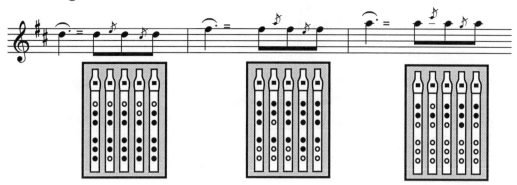

the merry blacksmith

CRAN

The **cran** is an ornament that is associated with piping. Since the manner in which notes are fingered on the pipes is similar to the whistle, the technique of cranning may be applied to the whistle. The cran is a series of cuts above the principal note. Each time a cut occurs a different finger is lifted, hence a different note will sound. The cran is usually performed on low D and E, where multiple fingerings for cuts are found. It may be substituted for a long or short roll, and in this text it will be notated as follows:

Cran in Simple Time

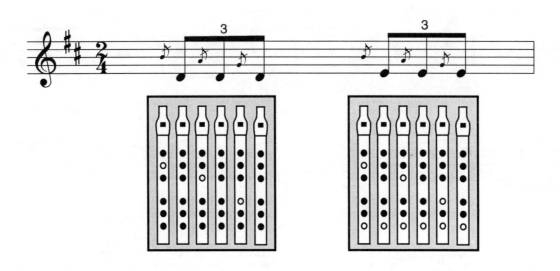

Cran in Compound Time

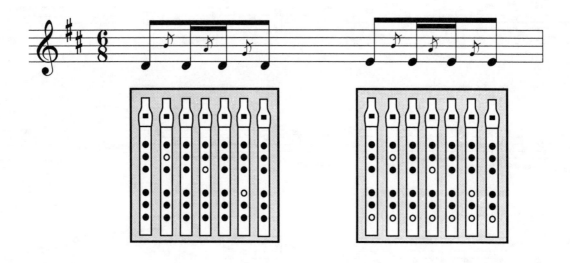

74

the threepenny bit

the girl who broke my heart

father dollard's hornpipe

styles

At one time playing styles were localized to particular counties or regions in Ireland. Over the years recorded media and social mobility have allowed stylistic homogenization to take place such that these traits are no longer regionalized. Stylistic differences range from skeletal and simple melodies to highly ornamented renditions, and from long and legato phrases to short and crisply articulated phrases. The following examples represent three very different styles of whistling. They illustrate the variety of ways ornamentation, phrasing, and rhythm may be combined to create a distinctive style. Remember that one of the great advantages of the folk tradition is that there is not a "correct way" to ornament a tune. A new variation is created each time a player performs. While this may seem like an obstacle to the novice it provides a continuous challege even for the accomplished player.

Stylistic Traits: Preponderance of tonguing and sparse ornamentation. Skeletal version of melody with little rhythmic alteration.

the walls of liscarroll

Stylistic Traits: Use of shorter phrases. Heavily ornamented. Played at a fast tempo.

over the moor to maggie

Stylistic traits: Requires legato playing (long phrases with little tonguing, and lots of breath control). Extra melodic note or triplet figure is used instead of other ornaments. Repeated notes under long phrases are articulated with a pulsation of the air stream rather than with the tongue. (See discussion of breath control for description of pulsations as they relate to vibrato.)

the reel of mullinavat

the process of variation

An important aspect of playing in the Irish style is the process of variation that occurs in nearly every solo performance. The music is essentially monophonic (i.e. single line melody), and a performance would seem monotonous unless some melodic variation occured in addition to rhythmic alteration. The skilled player of traditional music is a master of theme and variation. Skeletal phrases are retained; and, each time a section returns melodic, ornamental, and even rhythmic variation occurs. Apply the process of variation to each piece you play. Eventually your custom variations will assist you in developing your own unique playing style.

melodic variation

Changes made in repeated versions of a piece employ many of the melodic ornaments familiar to classically trained players. More often than not, only small details of a melody are changed. Players who have learned via the aural tradition do not consciously label these melodic ornaments, yet they are fluent with their usage. Commonly used ornaments are described here for ease in identification and application.

Neighbor Tone(s)

A note or notes inserted directly above or below two notes of the same pitch.

Passing Tone(s)

A note or notes inserted between two notes that are separated by a larger interval. The passing tones are added to fill-in the interval and create a more stepwise motion from one note to the next. The process of adding passing tones can be reversed by eliminating notes to simplify the line.

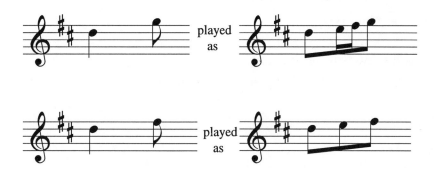

81

Added Chord Tone(s)

When ornamenting a note of long duration it is possible to insert notes belonging to chords implied by the melodic line. This is often done by ear when the player can hear suitable chordal accompaniments and add appropriate pitches. Guitar chords (when added above the musical line) can indicate suitable note additions. Observe how chord tones are inserted in the following example:

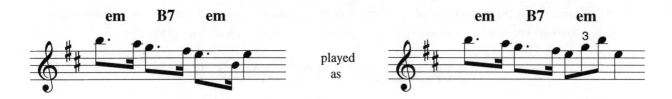

played
as

example for study

The following comparison of repeated sections in *The Turn Key* illustrates many of the typical changes that most players use when varying a melody:

a) Phrase/note changes for breathing (indicated by rest).
It is common practice to eliminate notes or change their duration in order to create a space where the player has ample time to breathe. Compare measures 4, 6, 8, and 10.

b) Slight melodic variation.
Passing tones and/or neighbor tones may be added to keep the rhythmic flow continuous. Compare measures 2, 5, 8, 9, and 12.

c) Use of the triplet figure.
Compare measures 2, 4, 5, 7, 8, 9 and 12.

d) Added grace notes.
Compare measures 1, 5, and 12.

e) Interchange of rolls and simpler graced figures.
Compare measures 2, 9, and 11.

f) Graced figures and triplets interchanged.
Staccato triplets substituted for rolls. Compare first measures.

g) Added chord tones.
Compare sixth measures.

the turn keg

M.M./D.G.

83

✠ slow airs and songs ✠

The Irish culture has a rich solo song tradition, and the lyrical, haunting melodies of many Irish songs are often played as instrumental solos. The term "air" is often used to label a song, although more recently the connotation for an air is a slow melody of great beauty. There are different approaches to playing slow airs. One approach attempts to copy the vocal inflection of a singer. Players may refer to the text of a song and use the lyrics as a reference point from which to play in an expressive song-style. Ancient Gaelic songs were usually sung without accompaniment. The singer elaborated upon a skeletal melody by adding long melismas (several notes per syllable) as well as other traditional vocal ornaments. The rubato (varied) tempo and ornate embellishment make this one of the most difficult styles to learn, and playing in this manner requires concentrated study and listening to traditional singing styles.

Another approach to playing slow airs treats the music itself—the rise and fall of the musical line and its expressive qualities as a separate entity. This is used more often in the ensemble setting. When the air is sung or played with accompanying instruments it does not lend itself well to the improvisatory old-style of singing. An instrumental ensemble places more chordal and metric restrictions on the performer. Ornaments are used, but not to the same extent as in traditional solo performance practice.

The brief mention made here of the song tradition must be supplemented with additional study and careful listening. There is no substitution for studying recorded and live sources when learning airs.

vibrato

An ornament that is frequently used in the performance of slow airs is the vibrato—the pulsation of a tone used to add expressive nuances to a musical line. Vibrato is used more often in slow airs than in dance music because the vibrato adds color and motion to notes of long duration.

There are two ways to achieve a vibrato on the whistle:

> 1) By wavering the fingers over two or more holes below the last closed hole on the instrument (a piping technique which evolved from control of sound through a bellows rather than with the breath).

> 2) By altering the air stream with the use of the diaphragm (major muscle used for breathing) and/or throat musculature.

fingered vibrato

Wavering of fingers over the tone-holes is the traditional method of creating vibrato, but only certain notes will respond to this procedure due to the nature of the fingering system on the instrument. The notes of **F#**, **G**, **A**, and **B** are best suited for application of this technique. Experiment with your instrument to find appropriate fingerings that will achieve the desired effect since all instruments do not respond in the same manner to changes in fingering.

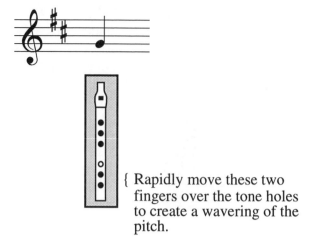

{ Rapidly move these two fingers over the tone holes to create a wavering of the pitch.

Note: It is also acceptable to trill on a note of long duration instead of using a vibrato. The trill is achieved by the rapid alternation of the principal note with the note directly above. It is notated with a trill symbol as in the example.

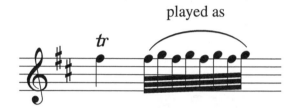

diaphragmatic vibrato

Gaining control of the diaphragm for purposes of expression can be learned through a regular practice regimen. As control over the musculature is achieved the vibrato may be added almost effortlessly by the performer. To practice the vibrato try the following exercise. Play a sustained pitch. Add evenly-spaced pulsations to the note by thrusting air from the diaphragm as if whispering the syllable "hah." Each thrust will cause a noticeable accentuation of the sustained note. Some players use the glottis or throat in this process.

Gradually increase the speed of the pulsations (as shown in the following example) until you are comfortable with the production and sound of the vibrato. The speed and use of the vibrato are largely a matter of personal taste. Listening to performances of slow airs by traditional players will give you a better idea of the various ways in which this expressive technique is used.

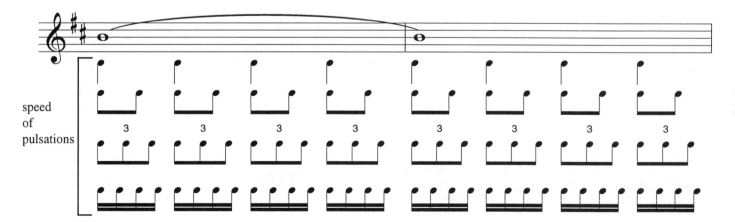

The following song may be used as a model for instrumental performance. *The Dear Irish Boy* is found in P.W. Joyce's *Old Irish Folk Music and Songs*. Joyce writes that the lyrics "smack of the classical schoolmaster, and there are a few strained expressions. Nevertheless, taken as a whole it is very pleasing: and its under-current of tenderness more than compensates for the spice of pedantry. The pathetic beauty of the air renders praise from me unnecessary." The air has endured through many variations of text, and is well-known by traditional players.

the dear irish boy

Recorded version played on an A whistle.

ᴛᴇxᴛ

1.

My Connor his cheeks are as ruddy as the morning;

The brightest of pearls do not outshine his teeth;

While nature with ringlets his mild brows adorning;

His hair Cupid's bowstrings and roses his breath.

CHORUS
> Smiling, beguiling, cheering, [and] endearing,
> Together oft over the mountains we strayed.
> By each other delighted, And fondly united,
> He listened all day to his dear Irish maid.

2.

No roebuck more swift could fly over the mountain;

No veteran bolder met dangers or scars;

He's sightly, he['s] sprightly, he's clear as the fountain;

His eyes beamed with love—Oh, he's gone to the wars.

CHORUS
> Smiling, beguiling, cheering, [and] endearing,
> Together oft over the mountains we strayed.
> By each other delighted, And fondly united,
> He listened all day to his dear Irish maid.

3.

The soft tuneful lark changed his notes into mourning;

The dark screaming owl now impedes my night's sleep;

While lonely I walk in the shades of the evening;

Till my Connor's return I will ne'er cease to weep.

CHORUS
> Smiling, beguiling, cheering, [and] endearing,
> Together oft over the mountains we strayed.
> By each other delighted, And fondly united,
> He listened all day to his dear Irish maid.

4.

The war is all over and he's not returning;

I fear that some envious plot has been laid;

Or that some cruel goddess has him captivated;

And has left here in mourning his dear Irish maid.

CHORUS
> Smiling, beguiling, cheering, [and] endearing,
> Together oft over the mountains we strayed.
> By each other delighted, And fondly united,
> He listened all day to his dear Irish maid.

The accompanying recording of *When I Followed a Lass* makes use of the "fingered vibrato" on notes of longer duration. The slide is also used as an important element of expression throughout the piece. The recorded version is paired with the single jig entitled *Barrack Hill*.

when i followed a lass

barrack hill

Sheebeg Sheemore is an Irish favorite that is said to be the first song written by the legendary Irish harper Turlough Carolan. The player should capture the song tradition when playing this tune, and attempt to play with all of the expressive qualities of a singer. The use of ornamentation will add a songlike character to the tune, especially the fingered vibrato and slides. The recorded version is followed by *The Stile of Ballylanders* and *Alexander's Hornpipe*.

sheebeg sheemore

the stile of ballglanders

90

alexander's hornpipe

other tunes

Other types of dance music such as: marches, quadrilles, strathspeys, flings, polkas, etc. are not included in this tutor. There are, however, many published collections of Irish music in which such tunes may be easily located. The same process of ornamentation and variation used in standard dance music applies to the performance of any piece that is to be played in the Irish style.

thanksgiving

This short and simple work evokes a humility that reflects the sentiment of its title. The recorded version is played on a whistle pitched in C. The A and B sections of *Thanksgiving* on the recording are punctuated with Gregorian chant—the *Agnus Dei* from a 13th century mass ordinary. This is followed by the double jig *Larry Grogan*.

agnus dei

A - gnus Dei   -   i, qui tol-   lis pec - ca - ta - mun-di;

mi- se- re- re   no   - bis. A - gnus De -   i, qui tol -   lis

pec - ca - ta   mun-di; mi- se- re - re   no   - bis. A - gnus De   - i,

qui tol -   lis pec - ca - ta   mun-di; do- na no - bis   pa   - cem.

larry grogan

1. 2.

1. 2.

93

The melody of the *Chanter's Tune* is characteristic of the pipes. The drone-like repetition of the note A is combined with a lightly ornamented melody that could easily be played on a pipe chanter. The recorded version is followed by *The Merry Harriers* and *The Threepenny Bit*.

the chanter's tune

, = breath mark

94

the merry harriers

95

the threepenny bit

96

pieces for study and practice

The remaining portion of this text contains pieces for study and practice. An unornamented "standard" version of each piece is presented (I) along with an ornamented variant (II). You may find it easier to practice the given ornaments until you are confident enough to experiment with your own version. As you develop your own unique style of playing you will rely less upon the ornamented variant and return to the "standard" version as a reference point from which to work.

the monaghan jig

I.

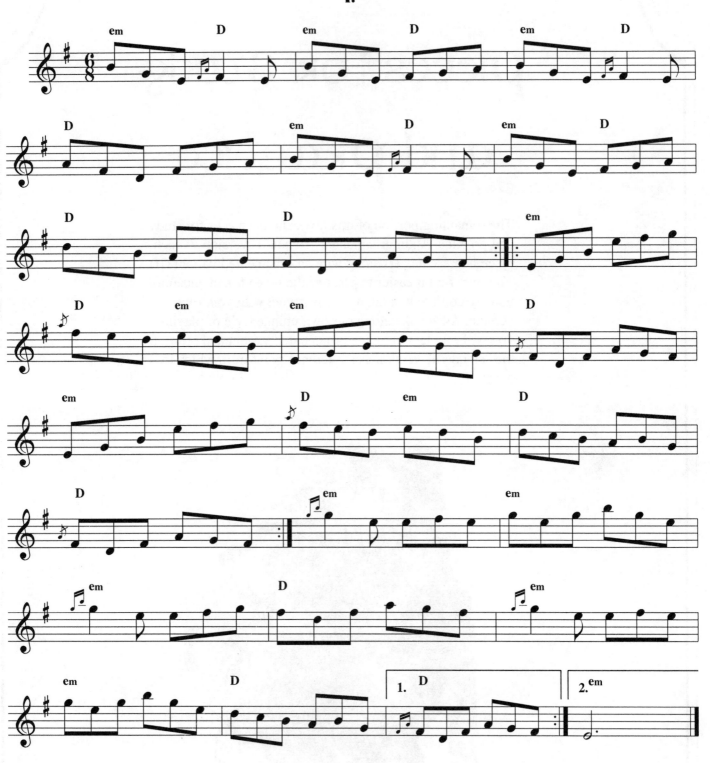

the monaghan jig

II.

the maid on the green

the musical priest

dunphy's hornpipe

I.

dunphy's hornpipe

II.

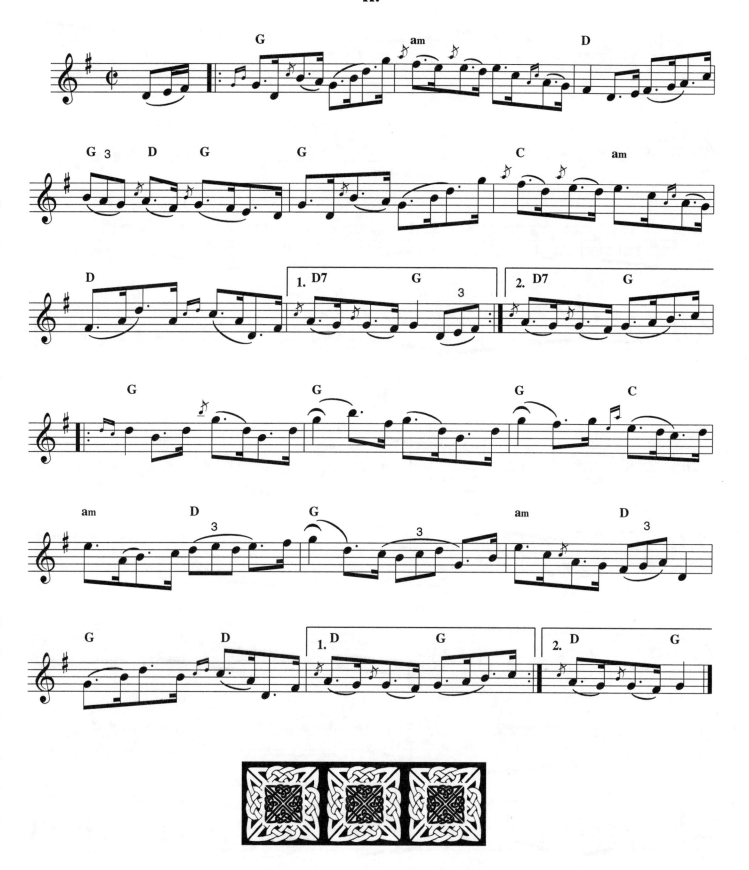

the cameronian reel

I.

II.

104

the humors of ballyconnell

I.

II.

maude miller

I.

II.

106

Father Jack Walsh (Tatter Jack Walsh)

107

the flogging reel

I.

the flogging reel

II.

sailor on the rock (johnny with the queer thing)

I.

II.

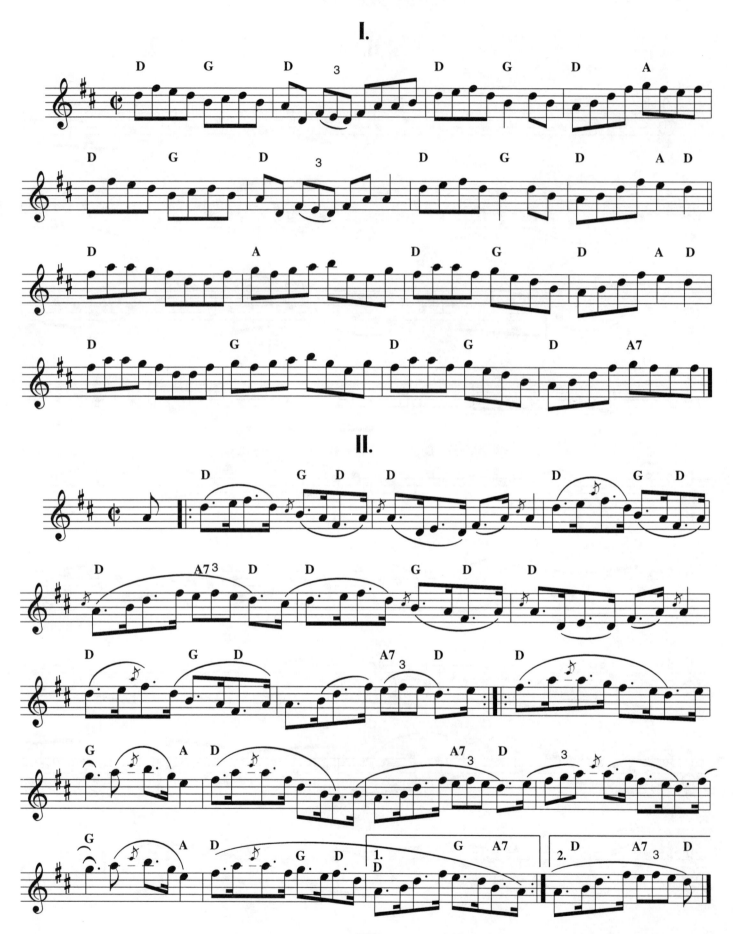

bogs of the town

I.

TRIM THE VELVET

I.

CRIM CHE VELVEC

II.

mooncoin jig

I.

mooncoin jig

II.

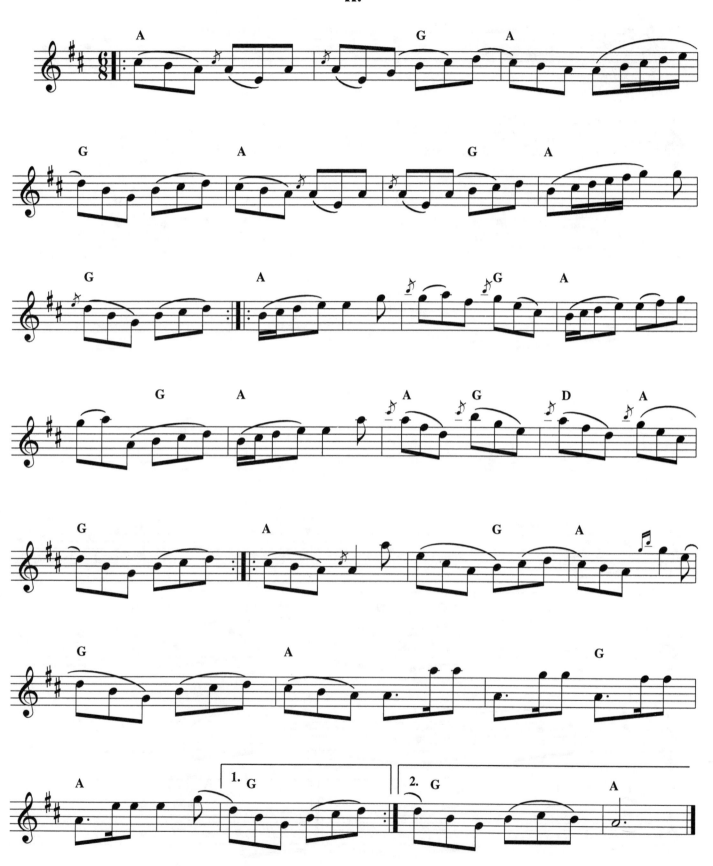

the tailor's wedding (the legacy jig)

I.

II.

jenny picking cockles

I.

II.

miss thornton's reel

I.

II.

the butcher's march

I.

II.

miss mcdonald

I.

miss mcdonald

II.

smash the windows

I.

smash the windows

II.

the queen of the fair

I.

the queen of the fair

II.

miss mccleod

I.

II.

humors of glendart

I.

II.

off she goes!

I.

II.

oh! hag gou have killed me

the fermog lasses

I.

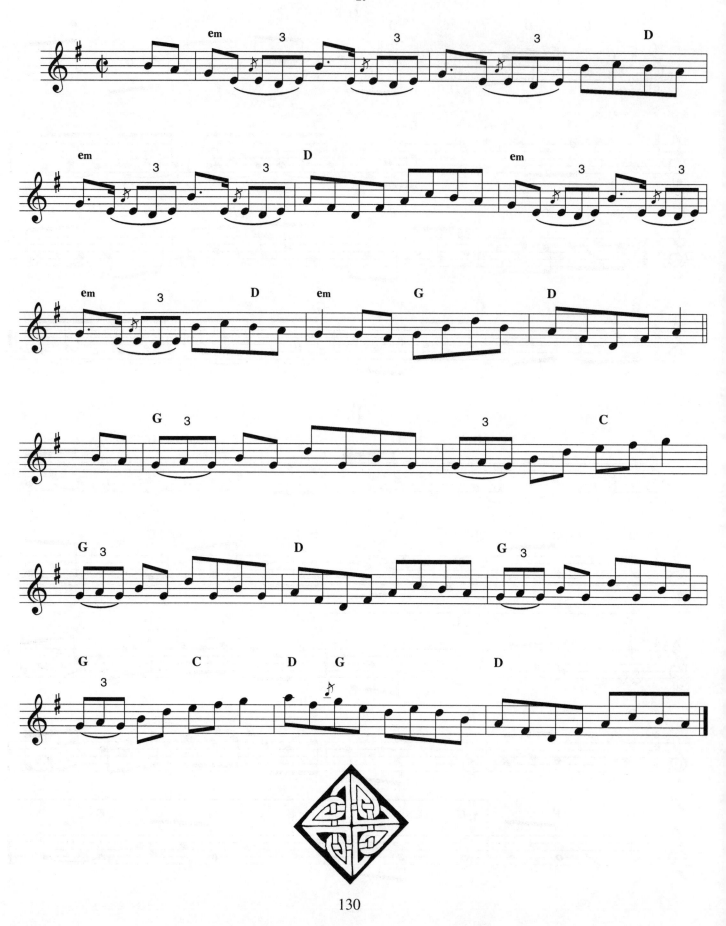

The fermog lasses

II.

the shannon breeze (rolling on the ryegrass)

I.

the shannon breeze (rolling on the ryegrass)

II.

the green groves of erin

I.

II.

Jenny's wedding

I.

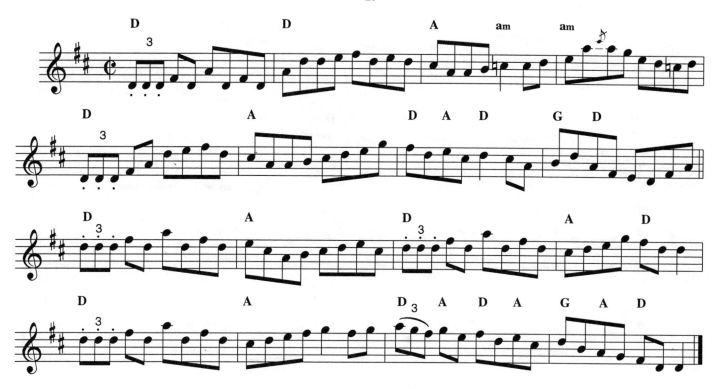

II.

bonnie kate

I.

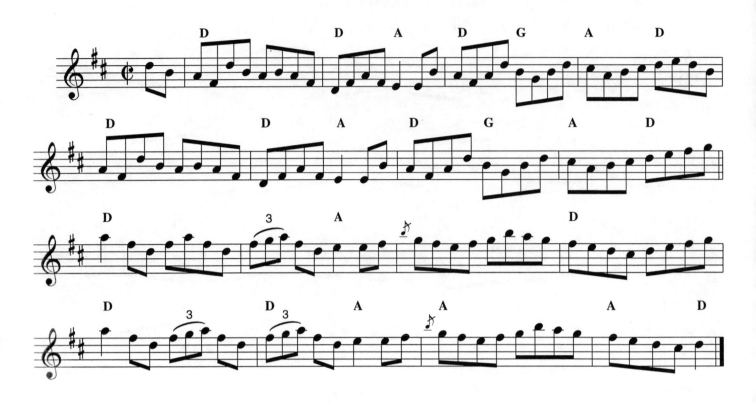

II.

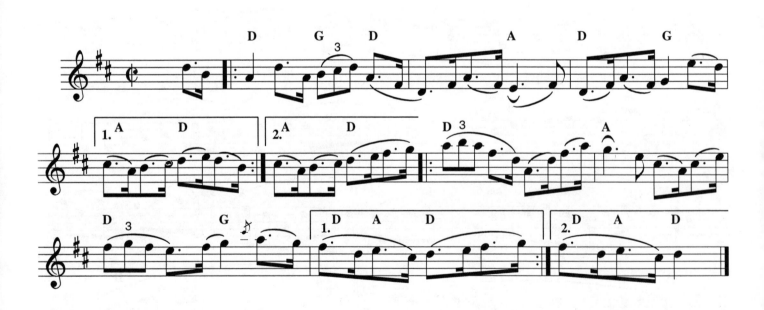

the templehouse

I.

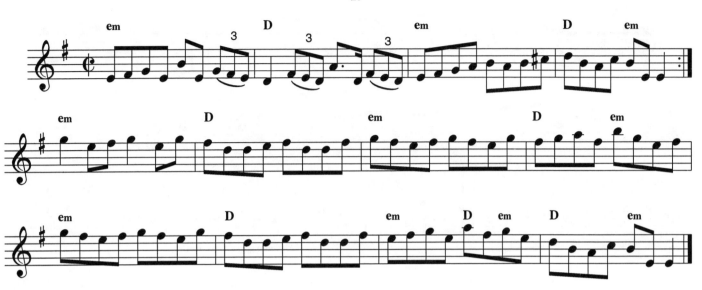

II.

The four-hand reel

I.

II.

138

the primrose lass

I.

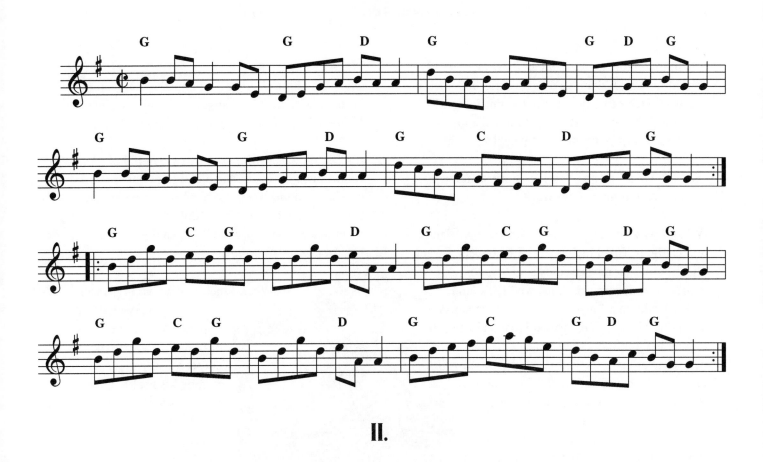

II.

epilogue

From a letter by the eminent American statesman, inventor, and author
Benjamin Franklin, dated November 10, 1779:

. . . In my opinion, we might all draw more good from [the world] than we do, and suffer less evil, if we would take care not to give too much for whistles. For to me it seems, that most of the unhappy people we meet with, are become so by neglect of that caution.

You ask what I mean? You love stories, and will excuse my telling one of myself.

When I was a child of seven years old, my friends, on a holiday, filled my pocket with coppers. I went directly to a shop where they sold toys for children; and, being charmed with the sound of a whistle, that I met by the way in the hands of another boy, I voluntarily offered and gave all my money for one. I then came home, and went whistling all over the house, much pleased with my whistle, but disturbing all the family. My brothers, and sisters, and cousins, understanding the bargain I had made, told me I had given four times as much for it as it was worth; put me in mind what good things I might have bought with the rest of the money; and laughed at me so much for my folly, that I cried with vexation; and the reflection gave me more chagrin than the whistle gave me pleasure.

This however was afterwards of use to me, the impression continuing on my mind; so that often, when I was tempted to buy some unnecessary thing, I said to myself, *Don't give too much for the whistle;* and I saved my money.

As I grew up, came into the world, and observed the actions of men, I thought I met with many, very many, who *gave too much for the whistle.*

When I saw one too ambitious of court favour, sacrificing his time in attendance on levees, his repose, his liberty, his virtue, and perhaps his friends, to attain it, I have said to myself, *This man gives too much for his whistle.*

When I saw another fond of popularity, constantly employing himself in political bustles, neglecting his own affairs, and ruining them by that neglect, *He pays, indeed,* said I, *too much for his whistle.*

If I knew a miser, who gave up every kind of comfortable living, all the pleasure of doing good to others, all the esteem of his fellow-citizens, and the joys of benevolent friendship, for the sake of accumulating wealth, *Poor man,* said I, *you pay too much for your whistle.*

When I met with a man of pleasure, sacrificing every laudable improvement of the mind, or of his fortune, to mere corporeal sensations, and ruining his health in their pursuit, *Mistaken man,* said I, *you are providing pain for yourself, instead of pleasure; you give too much for your whistle.*

If I see one fond of appearance, or fine clothes, fine house, fine furniture, fine equipages, all above his fortune, for which he contracts debts, and ends his career in a prison, *Alas!* say I, *he has paid dear, very dear, for his whistle.* When I see a beautiful, sweet-tempered girl married to an ill-natured brute of a husband, *What a pity,* say I, *that she should pay so much for a whistle!*

In short, I conceive that great part of the miseries of mankind are brought upon them by the false estimates they have made of the value of things, and by their *giving too much for their whistles.*

140

index of tunes

index by genre
airs

hornpipes

hornpipes continued

jigs
single jigs

double jigs

slip jig (hop jig)

Reels

set dances

other

 fingering chart

- ○ Open hole
- ● Closed hole
- ◑ Half hole

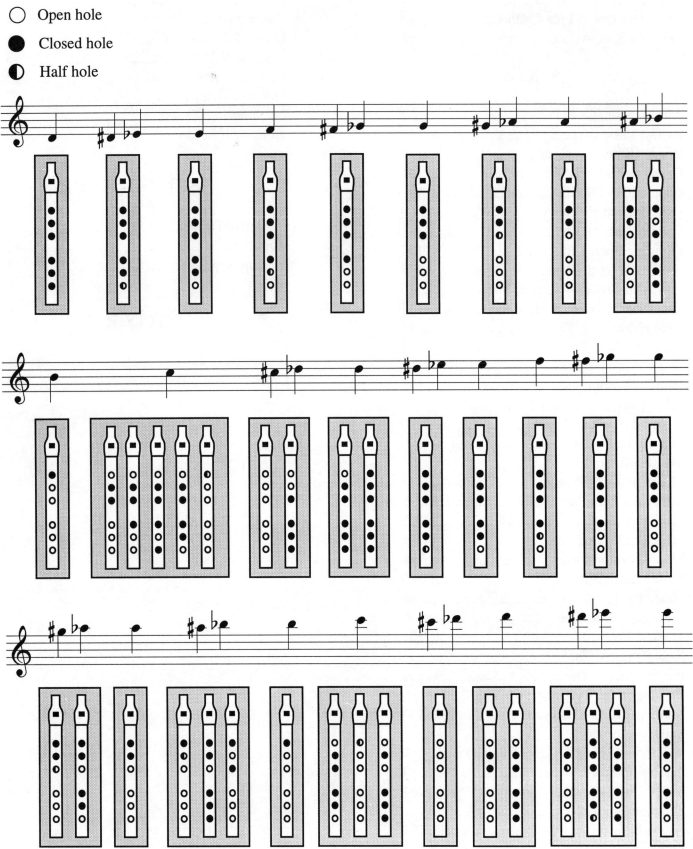

Note: Fingerings other than those listed on the above chart are possible.
Experiment with your whistle to find the best intonation and clarity of tone for each note.